The Marching
BAND NERDS
AWARDS

Nominations from **The 13th Chair**

Written By
DJ Corchin

Illustrated By
Dan Dougherty

The phazelFOZ Company, LLC

Published by The phazelFOZ Company, LLC.
Chicago, Illinois
www.phazelfoz.com

Library of Congress Number 2015955291

ISBN   9780996078184 (Hardcover)
       9780996078191 (Paperback)
       9780996078177 (eBook)

The
13th
Chair

Part of The 13th Chair's

BAND NERDS

Book Series

To Ken

Tradition

There are so many great traditions in music. They connect us with our past so that we can remember our journey. They can make us feel safe as we know that whatever happens, they will always be there. There's comfort in knowing that we can always fall back on the traditions of our musical culture. However, the inherent problem with Tradition is that it implies things need to always be done the way they've always been done. Often the only reason given is, "Well, it's tradition." I believe that when Tradition is the only reason for having itself, it's time to move on. There should always be purpose in what we do. It's how we move forward. In some cases, Tradition is used as an excuse to exclude. That's where we need to step in. If you don't believe a girl should be Drum Major simply because of tradition, not only are you wrong, you're in the way. When traditions get in the way of progress they are no longer traditions, they're obstacles. Don't be an obstacle. That never turns out well ;)

And the award goes to...

Most Intense Saluter

Bassoon Participation Award

Highest Flash

**Award For Most Consecutive Performances
Without Cleaning Their Uniform**

Loudest Trumpet Award

Softest Trumpet Award

Loudest Flute Award

**Most Exaggerated Story About
Almost Dying On The Field**

Most Intense Pass-Through

Best Player According To Their Own Parents

"Gets It The Most" Award

Best Stick Trick

One year ago...

Most Improved Player

Current year

Best Use Of Instrument

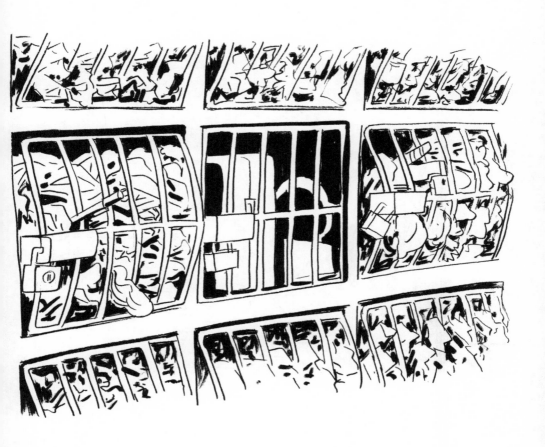

Most Organized Instrument Locker

Most Innovative Use Of Technology

Most Creative Use Of Sectional Time

Largest Spit Pool

Largest Spit Pool By A Woodwind

Most Courageous

Most Spectacular Plume

**Humanitarian Award For An Invention
Eliminating A Trombone's Blind Spot**

Straightest Company Front

First Clarinet Section Ever To Be Heard

**Award For Knowing The Most About Music
Theory, But The Least About How Much People
Care About Knowing The Most About Music Theory**

Most In Need Of Paper Clips To Straighten

Most Hours Practicing Marching

Highest Drum Major Podium

Oldest Drum Major Podium

Most Improved Flag Work

Least Improved Flag Work

Fastest Person With A Tuba

**Person Who Practices The Most
But Needs To The Least**

Best Drill Written For Oboe

Most Overdone Practice Wear

Most Difficult Pit Crew To Qualify For

Most Souped-Up Pit Vehicle

Most Flexible Flute

Best Example Of "Just Keep Going"

Hottest Practice Surface

**Most Consecutive Days Wearing
Black Jeans And Old-Timey Paperboy Hat
In 90 Degree Plus Weather**

Most Texts Sent During Rehearsal

Best Solution For The Perfect Horn Angle

**Best Timed "I Needed That" Conversation In The
Band Room After School**

**Designated Instrument To Be Left
Behind In Case Of A Fire**

Best "Show Face"

Longest Time Standing At Attention

Most Envious

Best Fort Builders

**Parent Who Always Has A Truck Available To
Borrow, But Is An Accountant**

Best Uniform Parent Team

Best Distance Keeper From Bad Breath

Biggest Knee Bend Before The Big Hit

Worst Bus Packing Job

Director Who Loves Technology The Most

Most Reflective Director Sunglasses

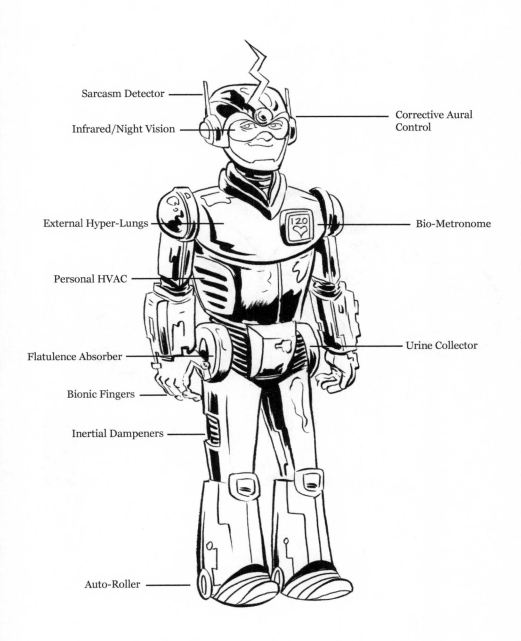

Sarcasm Detector

Infrared/Night Vision

Corrective Aural Control

External Hyper-Lungs

Bio-Metronome

Personal HVAC

Urine Collector

Flatulence Absorber

Bionic Fingers

Inertial Dampeners

Auto-Roller

Best Uniform

Best Boom That Shakes The Room

**Most Upset That Someone
Called Star Wars, Star Trek**

Most Amount Of Props

Best View

Most More Knowledgable Than Any Judge

Most Intense Counter

Most Likely To Star In Their Own Band Indie Film

**Best "If You Miss Your Spot Again And We Have
To Run It One More Time I'm Going To Kill You"
Face**

**Award For Person Who Already Assumes
They're Going To Win An Award But
The Season Just Started**

Best At Being Able To Spin Anything

**Most Frequently Gets The Sousa Case
With The Broken Wheel**

Most Acrobatic Solo

Most Overzealous Sound Designer

Least Complicated Show

Toughest Sax Player

Most Mallets Used In A Show By One Player

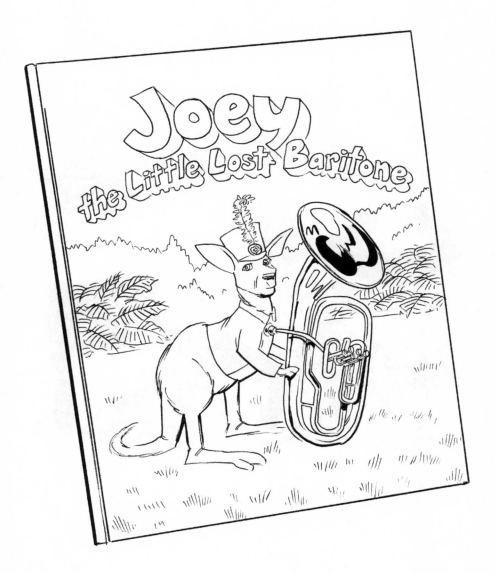

Best Children's Band Book

Calmest Pre-Show Ritual

Weirdest Pre-Show Ritual

Actual Flight Achievement

Best Use of Saber

Latest Time Returning From A Competition

Largest Step Size
1 to 5

Stupid Stereotype Destroyer Award

Best Dreamer

Best Place To Be

**Peace with a whole lotta hair grease.
See ya.**